MW00387284

IN RECITAL®
Duets
Volume One

ABOUT THE SERIES • A NOTE TO THE TEACHER

The *In Recital® Duets* series focuses on fabulous duet repertoire intended to motivate your students. All volumes of *In Recital®* address the issue of motivating students with attainable goals. The comprehensively leveled curriculum makes that possible, and this duet series offers a wonderful repertoire opportunity for your students. You will find original duets, duet arrangements of popular pieces, and duet arrangements of famous classical themes. There are equal-part duets as well as unequal-part duets that can be played by the teacher or a more advanced student. The duets in this series address a wide variety of different musical and technical issues, giving you the selection needed to accommodate your students' needs and plan recital repertoire for the entire year. The series provides practice tips, rehearsal suggestions, and duet performance strategies to help your students be successful!

Use the enclosed CD as a teaching and motivational tool. Have your students listen to the recording and discuss interpretation with you! To learn how to use the CD as a valuable practice aid, turn to page 40.

THE F·J·H MUSIC COMPANY INC.
Frank J. Hackinson

Production: Frank J. Hackinson
Production Coordinator: Philip Groeber
Art Direction: Terpstra Design, San Francisco
Cover and Interior Art Concepts: Helen Marlais
Cover and Inside Illustrations: Keith Criss
Engraving: Tempo Music Press, Inc.
Printer: Tempo Music Press, Inc.

ISBN 1-56939-515-2

ORGANIZATION OF THE SERIES
IN RECITAL® DUETS

The series is carefully leveled into the following six categories: Early Elementary, Elementary, Late Elementary, Early Intermediate, Intermediate, and Late Intermediate. Each of the works has been selected for its artistic as well as its pedagogical merit.

Book One — Early Elementary, reinforces the following concepts:

- Basic notes such as quarter, half, dotted half, and whole notes are used.

- $\frac{3}{4}$ and $\frac{4}{4}$ time signatures.

- Students experience movement up and down the keyboard, with *8va* signs.

- Students play with both a detached and smooth touch.

- Most of the pieces call for limited use of hands-together playing.

- Pieces reinforce basic musical terminology and symbols such as *forte* and *piano*.

- Pieces use middle C and G position as well as other basic hand positions.

- Keys — C major, G major, and F major (written using accidentals instead of key signatures).

THE BENEFITS OF PLAYING DUETS

Duets are good for a student's sense of rhythm and ensemble. They learn to "catch" the rhythm — whether it is fast or slow, and they learn to listen to each other and produce subtle changes in dynamics and tempo. Furthermore, playing duets gives students the opportunity to sense their partner's musicianship. The hands-on experience of interacting with another musician and enjoying each other's spirit in the music is an important step in developing their understanding of musicality. Duets can be an integral ingredient in lighting the musical fire!

An ensemble recital is great fun, and a mixed program of solos and duets provides variety for the audience. Playing duets for friends, family, other students, or for school is a wonderful way to spread the joy of music.

Enjoy all of these wonderful duets!

Most of the pieces in this book were arranged as equal-part duets. The only two that are unequal-part duets, with the *secondo* part to be played by the teacher or a more advanced student, are *Yankee Doodle* and *Take Me Out to the Ball Game*.

TABLE OF CONTENTS

	Recital Category	Composer	Arranger	Page	Performance CD Track	Primo Track	Secondo Track
About Duet Playing	Helen Marlais			4-5			
Ode to Joy, Theme from *Symphony No. 9*	Equal Part Duet	Ludwig van Beethoven	Timothy Brown	6-9	1	9	10
Are You Sleeping? (*Frére Jacques*)	Equal Part Duet	French Round	Edwin McLean	10-13	2	11	12
Yankee Doodle	Unequal Part Duet	Traditional American	Melody Bober	14-17	3	13	14
Double Trouble	Equal Part Duet	Kevin Olson		18-21	4	15	16
Row, Row, Row Your Boat	Equal Part Duet	Traditional	Robert Schultz	22-25	5	17	18
Roller Coaster Ride	Equal Part Duet	Melody Bober		26-29	6	19	20
Bingo	Equal Part Duet	Traditional	Kevin Olson	30-33	7	21	22
Take Me Out to the Ball Game	Unequal Part Duet	M: Albert von Tilzer W: Jack Norworth	Edwin McLean	34-37	8	23	24
About the Composers/ Arrangers				38-39			
Using the CD	Helen Marlais			40			

Primo parts played by Helen Marlais; Secondo parts played by Christine Kim.

A Special Note to Students:

This collection of duets is for you to play and enjoy! All of the duets are different in character, and each creates a different mood.

Tips for Practicing at Home:

Here are a few practice suggestions for you to do at home. They will help you play these duets successfully with a partner:

1) Practice your part until you can play it without stopping (with correct notes and steady rhythm) before you go to your lesson.

2) Mark in specific starting locations throughout each duet to make your rehearsal easier and more effective. Start at these various locations when you practice at home so you will be ready for your rehearsal.

3) Listen to the performance track on the CD recording to familiarize yourself with the duet. In order to prepare well, first practice your part, and then play along with the recording of your own part that you will hear on the CD. Then play your part along with the recording of your duet partner's part in order to really be prepared!

Tips for Practicing with your Duet Partner:

1) In order for the ensemble to work well and look professional, start with your hands in your lap. You and your partner should bring your hands up to the keyboard at the same time. Breathe together to begin the duet for perfect synchronization! (Don't count off.) After playing, both you and your partner should end with your hands in your lap.

2) Decide with your ensemble partner who has the melody at any given moment. Ask yourselves, "Which part should be brought out over the other part?"

   After you have played the duet, ask yourselves, "What was the balance like between the melody and the accompaniment throughout the entire piece?"

3) While you are practicing, you might wish to count together; this way you'll be sure to play together at the same tempo and without stopping.

4) Really listen to your duet partner's part so that you both play completely together. Above all, enjoy making music with another person! If you find you are having trouble doing this, you need to practice even more at home, with and without the CD!

5) Poise at the piano — decide with your partner how you will walk on stage, stand at the piano, and bow to the audience. If you practice this often, you will be very polished at the performance!

ODE TO JOY
Theme from *Symphony No. 9*

Secondo

Ludwig van Beethoven
arr. Timothy Brown

With much joy (♩ = ca. 152)
Play both hands one octave lower throughout

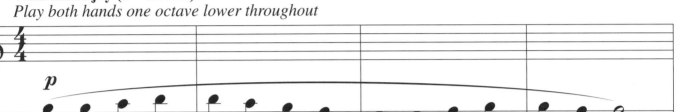

gradually   get   louder

FF161

JOY!

ODE TO ♪
Theme from *Symphony*

Primo

With much joy (♩ = ca. 152)

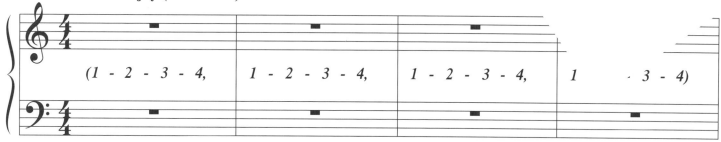

(1 - 2 - 3 - 4, 1 - 2 - 3 - 4, 1 - 2 - 3 - 4, 1 · 3 - 4)

5 *Play both hands one octave higher throughout*

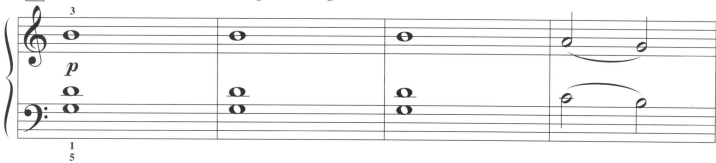

9

gradually get louder

13

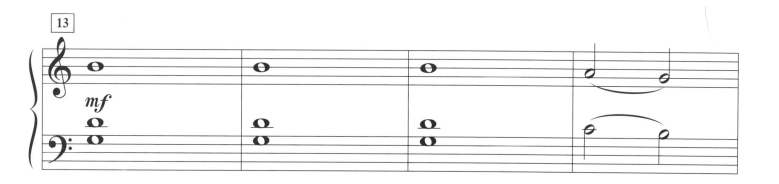

F1610

Primo

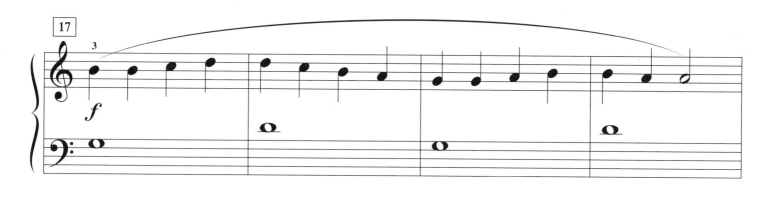

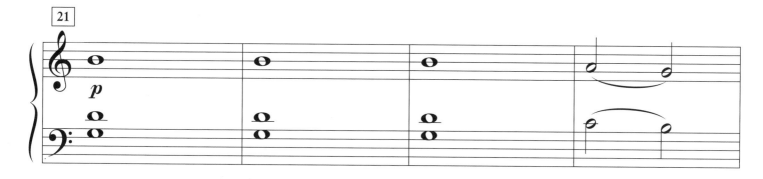

get louder

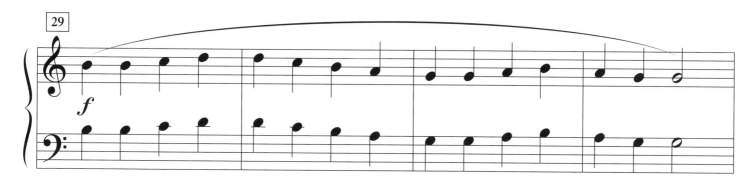

ARE YOU SLEEPING?

(Frère Jacques)

Secondo

French Round
arr. Edwin McLean

Moderately flowing (♩ = ca. 96)

Play both hands one octave lower throughout

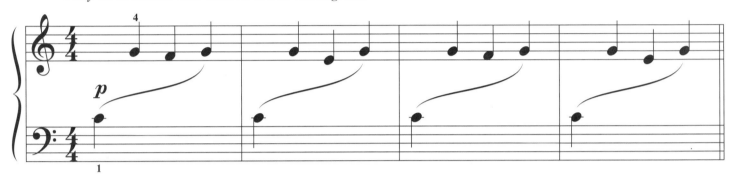

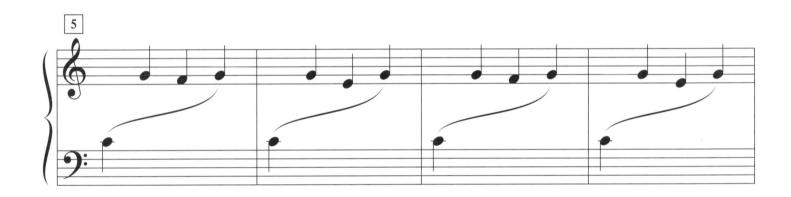

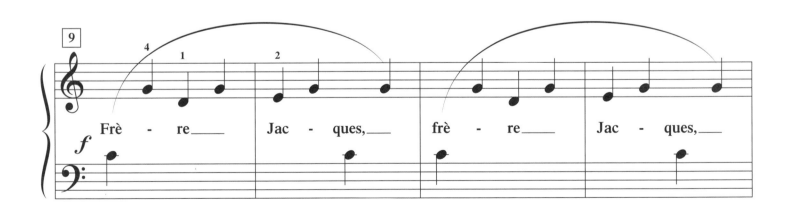

FF1616

ARE YOU SLE

(Frère Jacques)

Primo

Moderately flowing ($\quad$ = ca. 96)

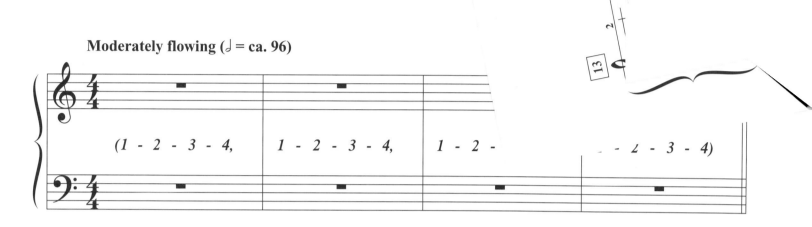

(1 - 2 - 3 - 4,   1 - 2 - 3 - 4,   1 - 2 -   - 2 - 3 - 4)

5 *Play both hands one octave higher throughout*

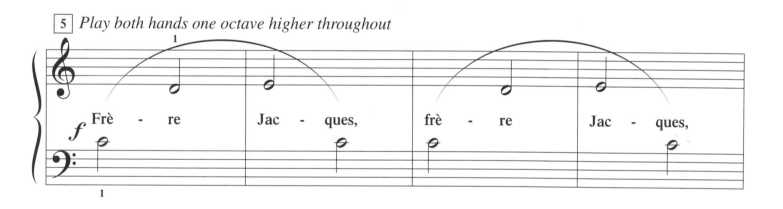

Frè - re   Jac - ques,   frè - re   Jac - ques,

9

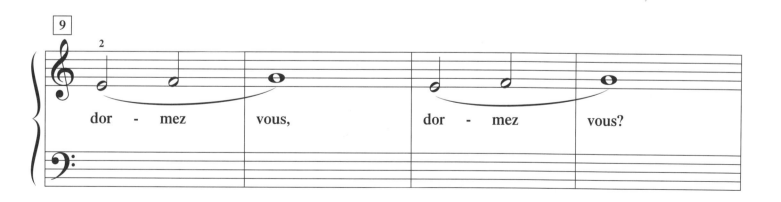

dor - mez   vous,   dor - mez   vous?

F1610

Secondo

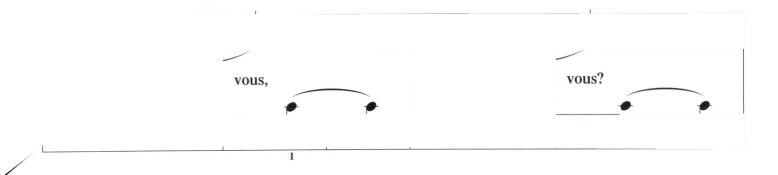

vous,   vous?

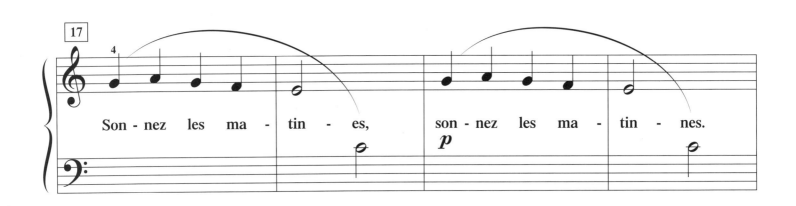

17

Son - nez les ma - tin - es,   son - nez les ma - tin - nes.

p

21

Din,   din,   don.   Din,   din,   don.

even quieter

Primo

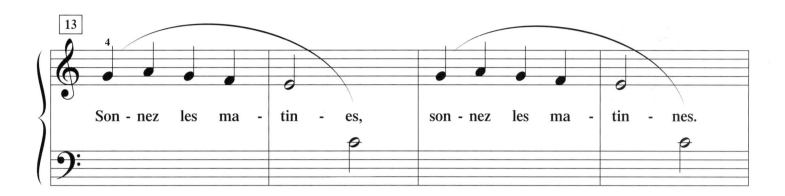

Son - nez les ma - tin - es, son - nez les ma - tin - nes.

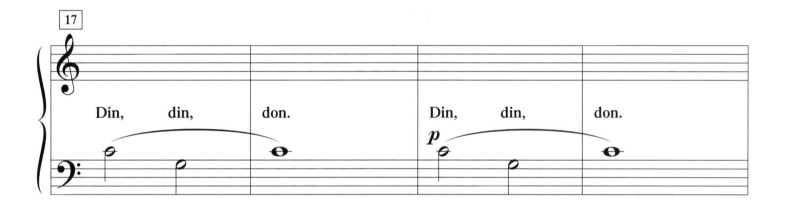

Din, din, don. Din, din, don.

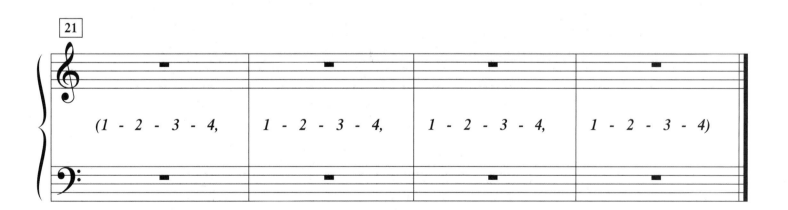

(1 - 2 - 3 - 4, 1 - 2 - 3 - 4, 1 - 2 - 3 - 4, 1 - 2 - 3 - 4)

YANKEE DOODLE

Secondo

Traditional American
arr. Melody Bober

March (♩ = ca. 138-144)

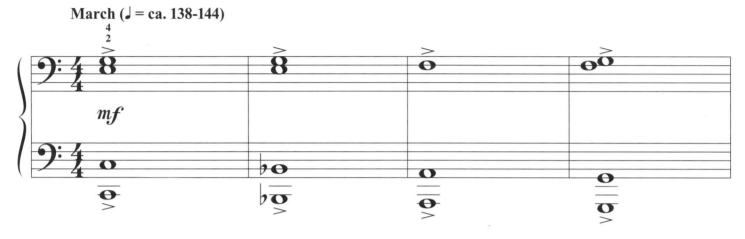

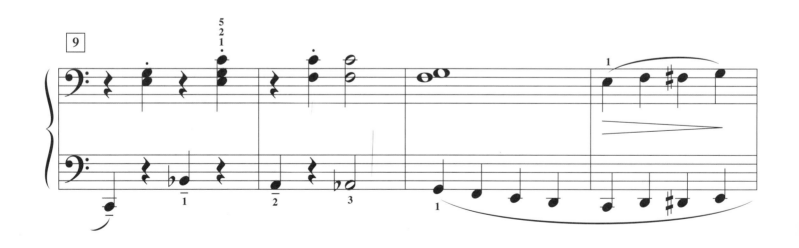

FF1610

...stuck a feather in his hat and called it macaroni.

YANKEE DOOL

Primo

March (♩ = ca. 138-144)
Play both hands one octave higher throughout

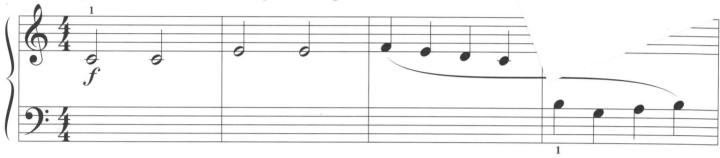

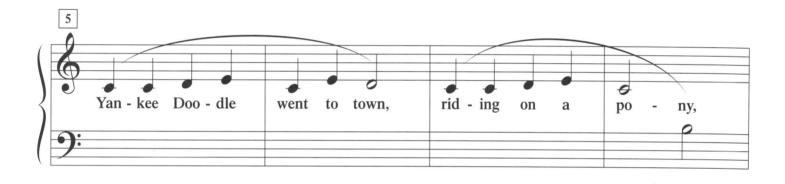

Yan - kee Doo - dle went to town, rid - ing on a po - ny,

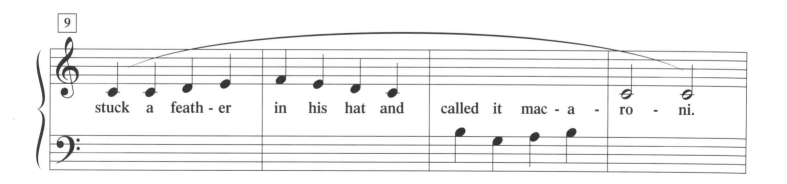

stuck a feath - er in his hat and called it mac - a - ro - ni.

FF1610

Secondo

Primo

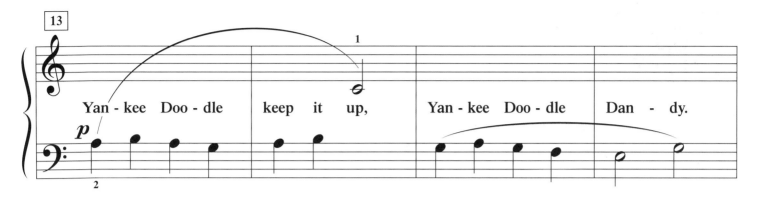

Yan - kee Doo - dle   keep it up,   Yan - kee Doo - dle   Dan - dy.

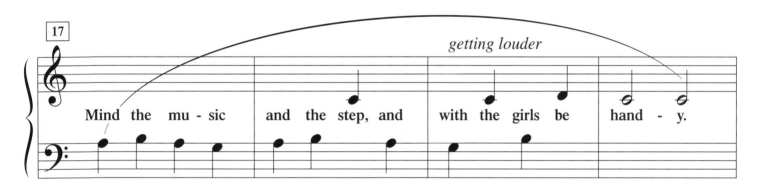

getting louder

Mind the mu - sic   and the step, and   with the girls be   hand - y.

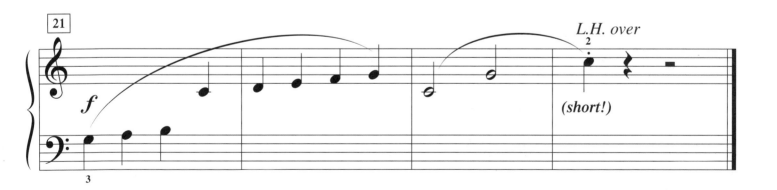

L.H. over

(short!)

DOUBLE TROUBLE

Secondo

Kevin Olson

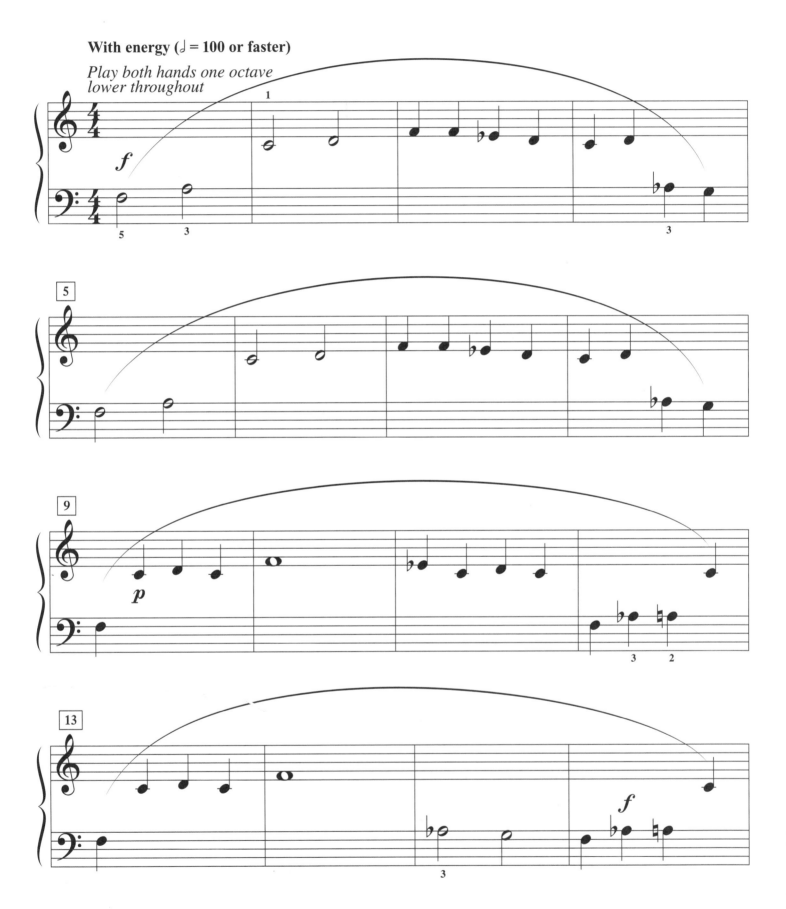

FF1610

DOUBLE TROUBLE

Primo

Kevin Olson

With energy (♩ = 100 or faster)

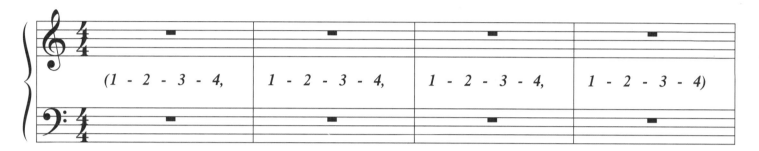

(1 - 2 - 3 - 4,   1 - 2 - 3 - 4,   1 - 2 - 3 - 4,   1 - 2 - 3 - 4)

Play both hands one octave higher throughout

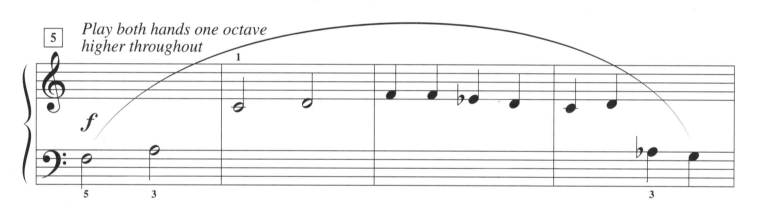

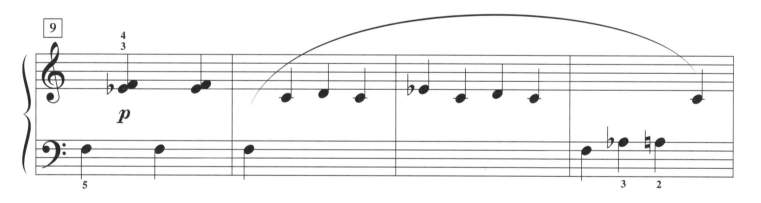

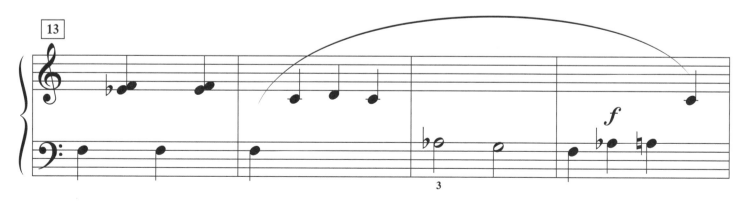

Secondo

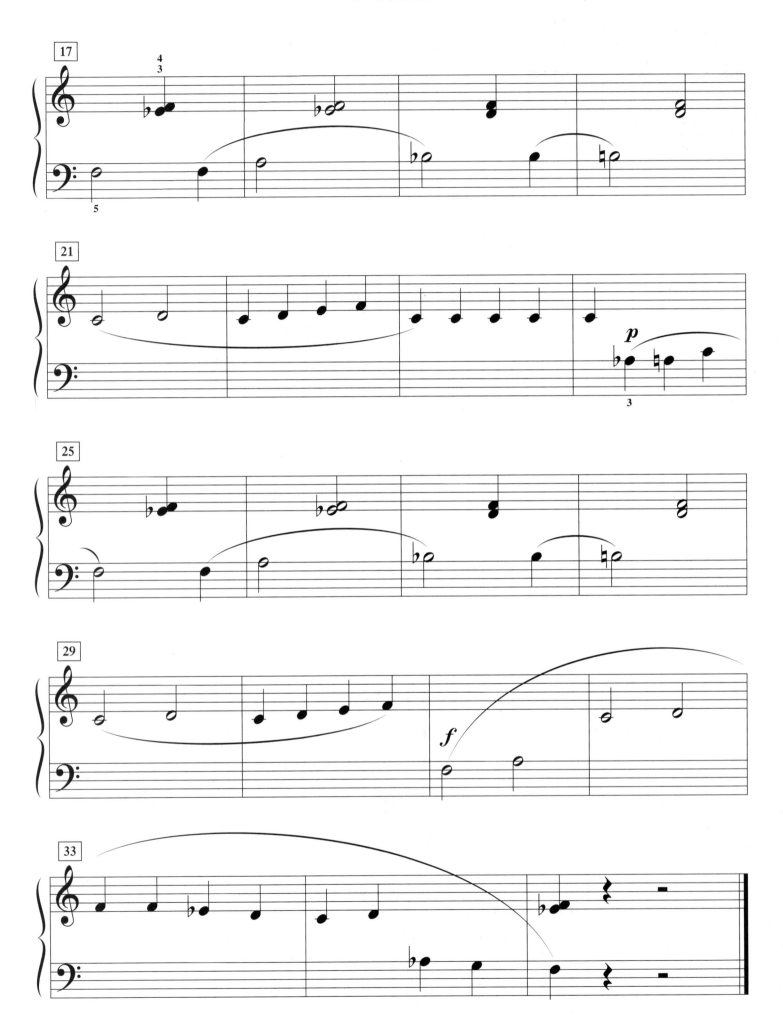

Primo

Row, Row, Row Your Boat

Secondo

Traditional
arr. Robert Schultz

Flowing (♩. = ca. 63)

FF16

Life is but a dream!

Row, Row, Row Your Boat

Primo

Traditional
arr. Robert Schultz

Flowing (♩. = ca. 63)

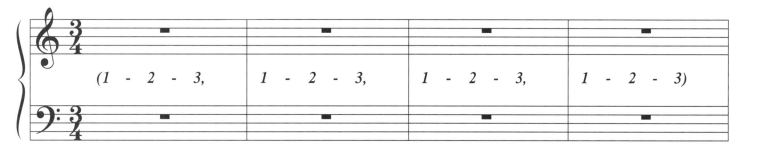

(1 - 2 - 3,   1 - 2 - 3,   1 - 2 - 3,   1 - 2 - 3)

5 *Play both hands one octave higher throughout*

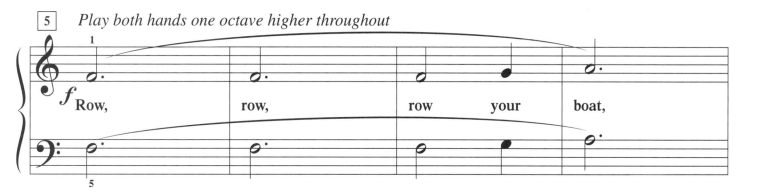

f Row,   row,   row   your   boat,

9

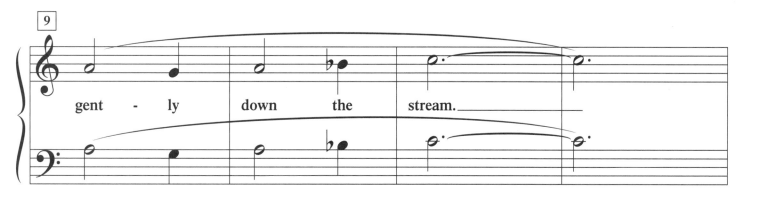

gent - ly   down   the   stream.

13

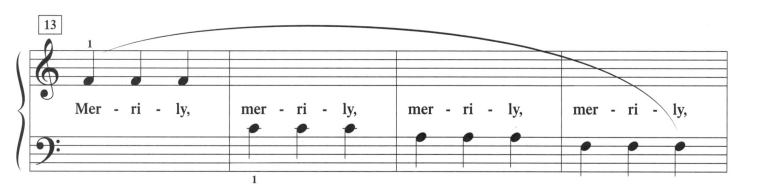

Mer - ri - ly,   mer - ri - ly,   mer - ri - ly,   mer - ri - ly,

Secondo

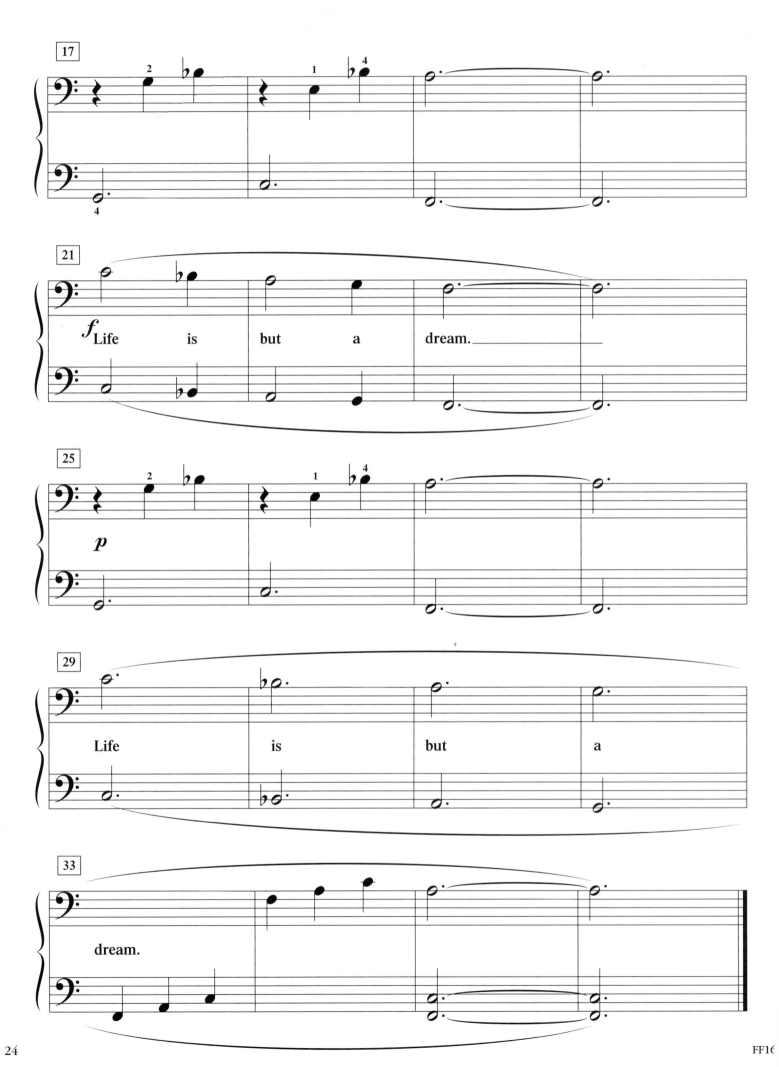

Primo

play smoothly until the end

1610   25

ROLLER COASTER RIDE

Secondo

Melody Bober

Cheerfully (♩ = 200 or faster)

Play both hands one octave lower throughout

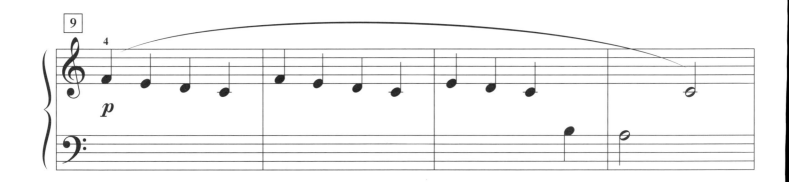

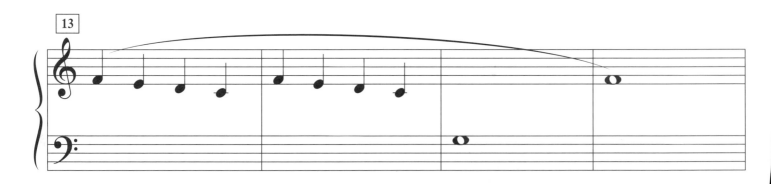

FF1

ROLLER COASTER RIDE

Primo

Melody Bober

Cheerfully (♩ = 200 or faster)
Play both hands one octave higher throughout

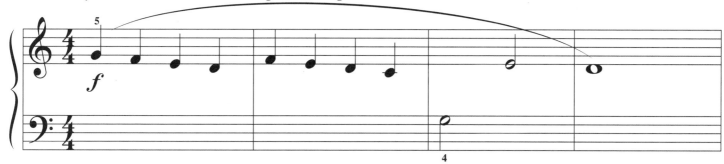

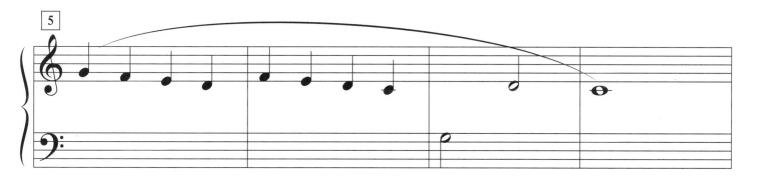

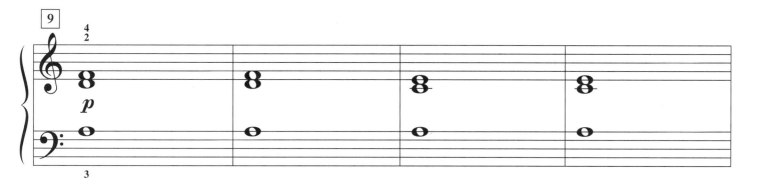

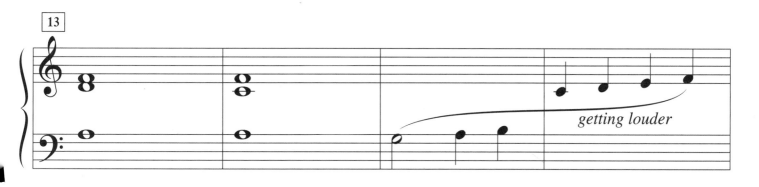

1610

Secondo

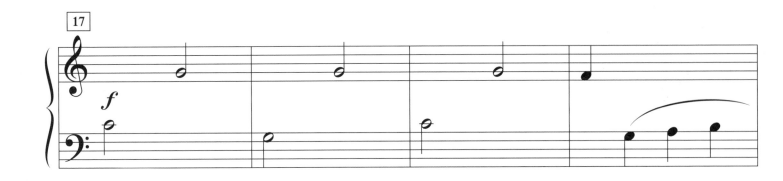

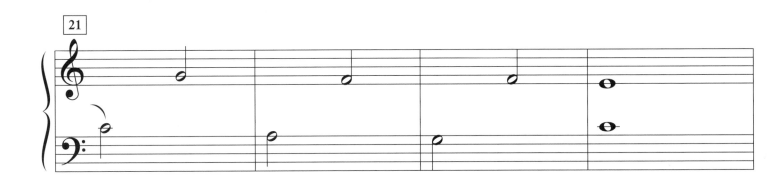

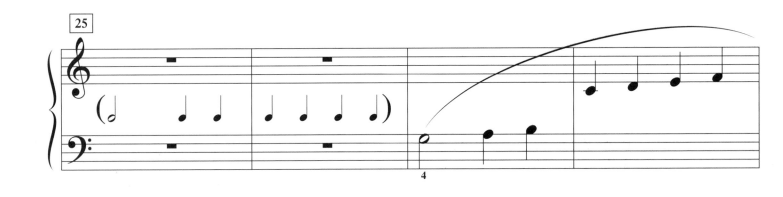

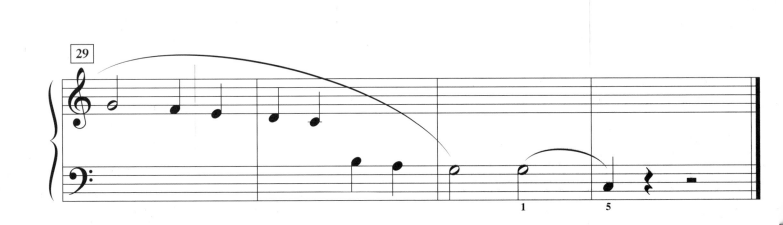

Primo

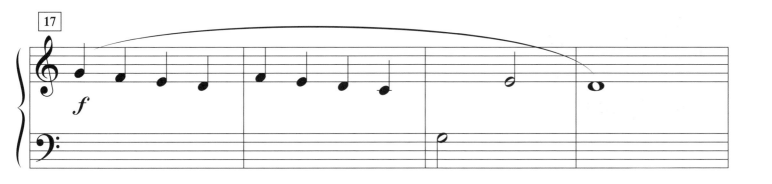

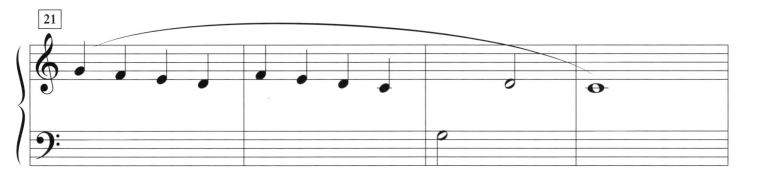

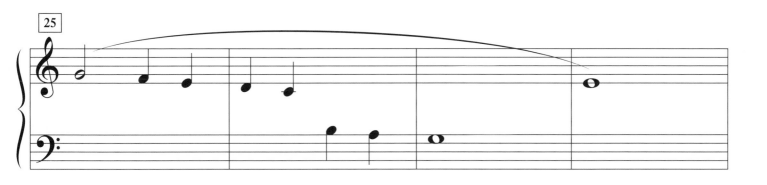

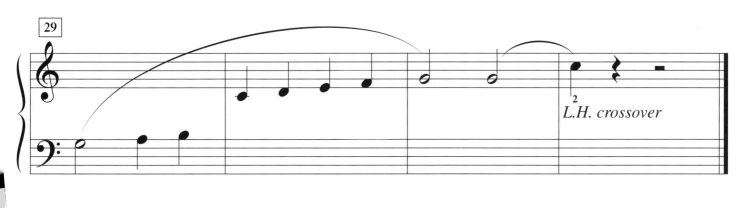

BINGO

Secondo

Traditional
arr. Kevin Olson

With energy (♩ = 132 or faster)

Play both hands one octave lower throughout

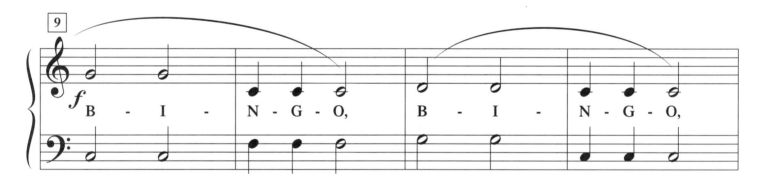

B - I - N - G - O,   B - I - N - G - O,

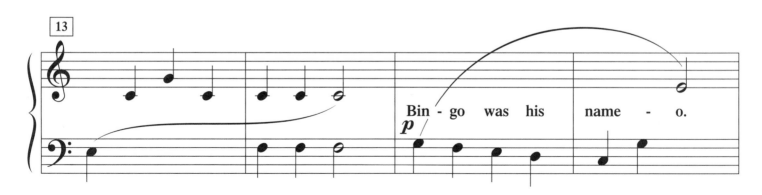

Bin - go was his name - o.

FF16

BINGO

Primo

Traditional
arr. Kevin Olson

With energy (♩ = 132 or faster)
Play both hands one octave higher throughout

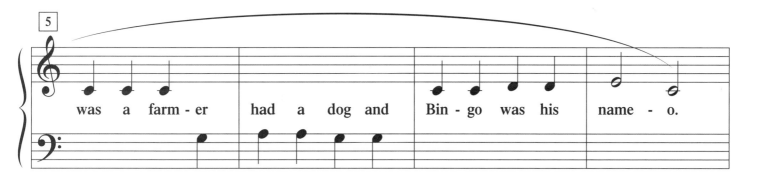

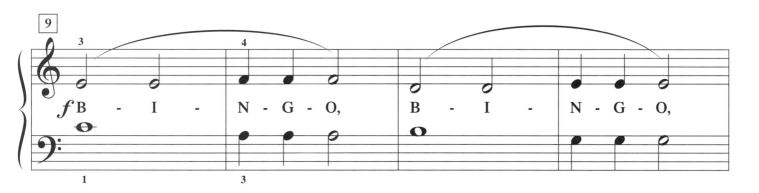

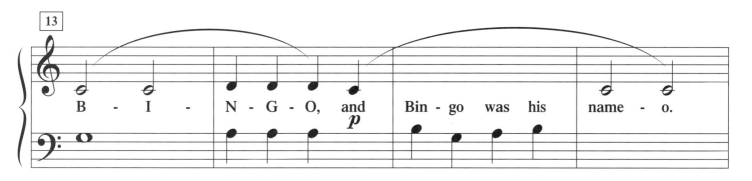

Secondo

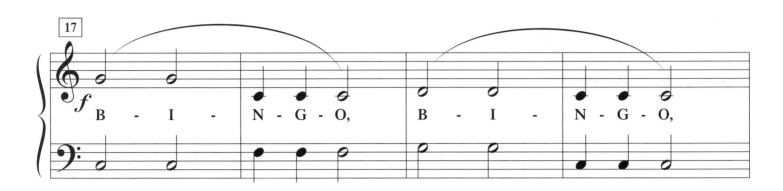

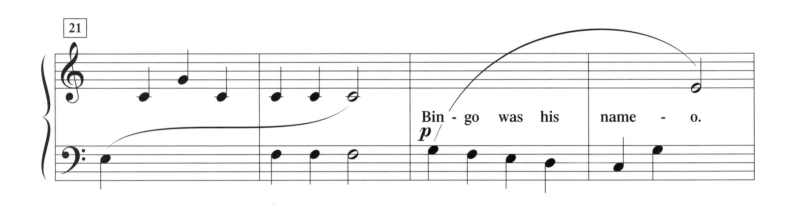

FF1C

Primo

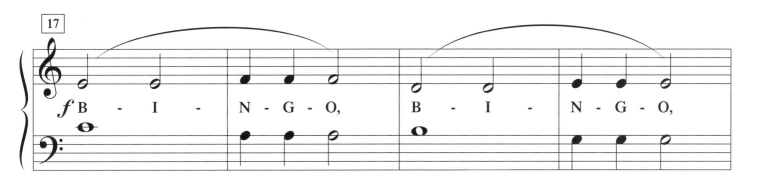

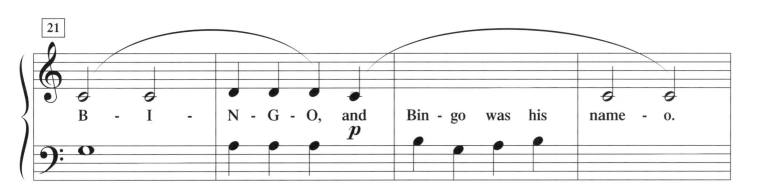

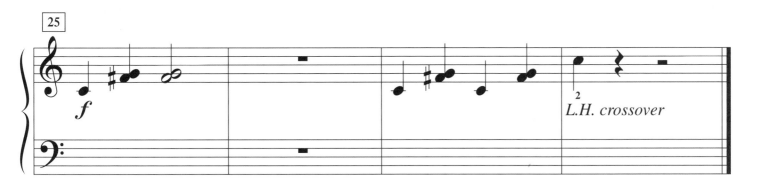

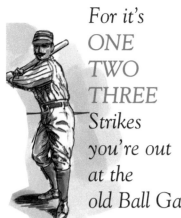

Take Me Out to the Ball Game

Secondo

Words: Jack Norworth
Music: Albert von Tilzer
arr. Edwin McLean

FF10

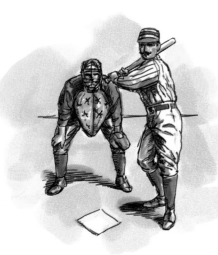

TAKE ME OUT TO THE BALL GAME

Primo

Words: Jack Norworth
Music: Albert von Tilzer
arr. Edwin McLean

Brightly (♩. = ca. 63)
Play both hands one octave higher throughout

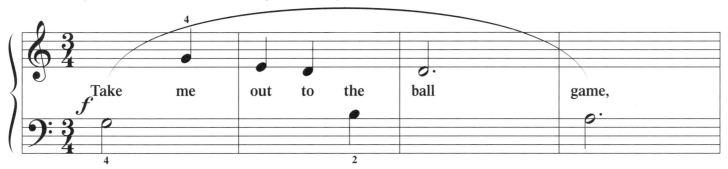

Take me out to the ball game,

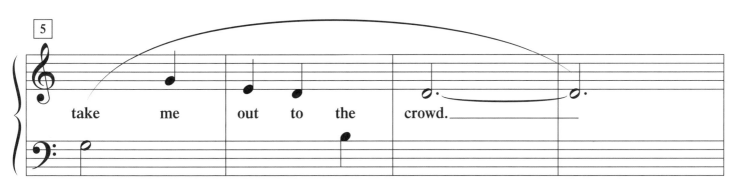

take me out to the crowd.

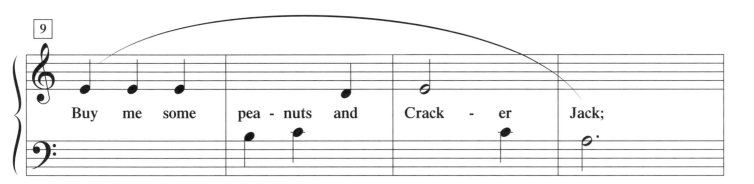

Buy me some pea - nuts and Crack - er Jack;

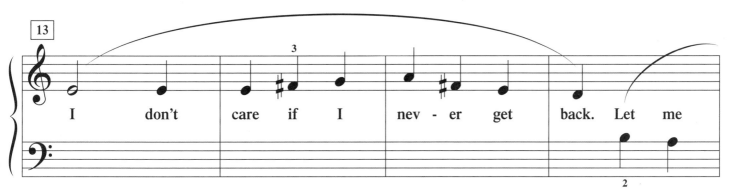

I don't care if I nev - er get back. Let me

Secondo

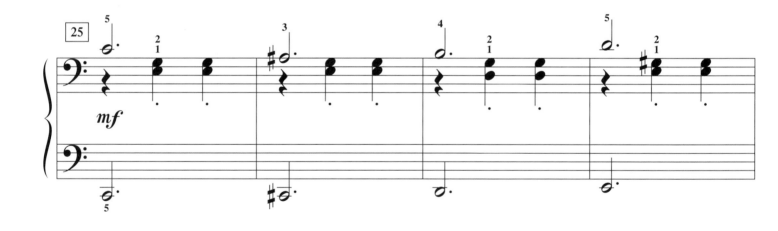

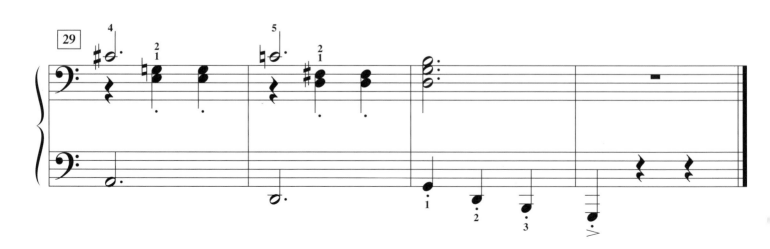

Primo

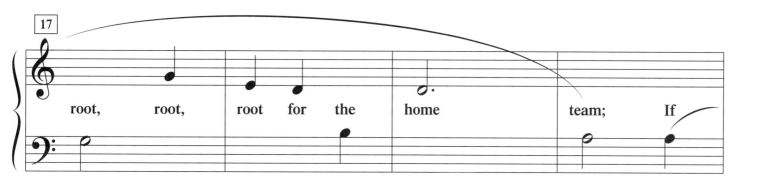

root,　　root,　　root for the　　home　　team;　If

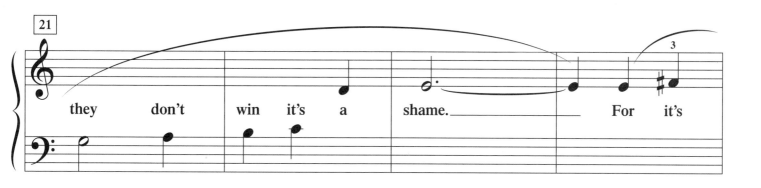

they　　don't　　win it's a　shame.＿＿＿＿＿　For it's

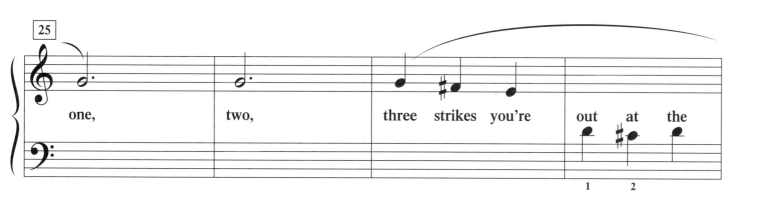

one,　　two,　　three strikes you're　out at the

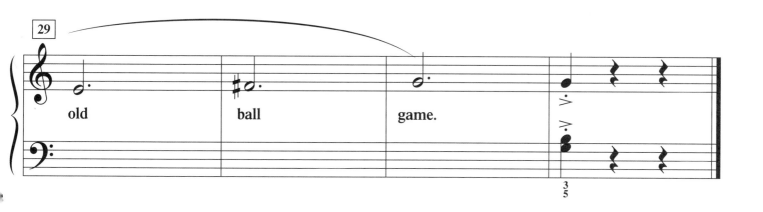

old　　ball　　game.

Melody Bober

Piano instructor, music teacher, composer, clinician—Melody Bober has been active in music education for over 25 years. As a composer, her goal is to create exciting and challenging pieces that are strong teaching tools to promote a lifelong love, understanding, and appreciation for music. Pedagogy, ear training, and musical expression are fundamentals of Melody's teaching, as well as fostering composition skills in her students. Melody graduated with highest honors from the University of Illinois with a degree in music education, and later received a master's degree in piano performance. She maintains a large private studio, performs in numerous regional events, and conducts workshops across the country. She and her husband Jeff reside in Minnesota.

Timothy Brown

Composition has always been a natural form of self-expression for Timothy Brown. His Montessori-influenced philosophy has greatly helped define his approach as a teacher and composer of educational music. His composition originates from a love of improvisation at the piano and his personal goal of writing music that will help release the student's imagination.

Mr. Brown holds two degrees in piano performance, including a master's degree from the University of North Texas. His many honors include a "Commissioned for Clavier" magazine article, and first prize award in the Fifth Aliénor International Harpsichord Competition for his solo composition *Suite Española*. As a clinician, Mr. Brown has presented numerous clinics and most recently represented FJH Music with his presentation at the 2000 World Piano Pedagogy Conference. Currently living in Dallas, Mr. Brown teaches piano and composition at the Harry Stone Montessori Magnet School. He frequently serves as an adjudicator for piano and composition contests, and performs with his wife as duo-pianists.

Edwin McLean

Edwin McLean is a freelance composer living in Chapel Hill, North Carolina. He is a graduate of the Yale School of Music, where he studied with Krzysztof Penderecki and Jacob Druckman. He also holds a master's degree in music theory and a bachelor's degree in piano performance from the University of Colorado.

Mr. McLean has been the recipient of several grants and awards: The MacDowell Colony, the John Work Award, the Woods Chandler Prize (Yale), Meet the Composer, Florida Arts Council, and many others. He has also won the Aliénor Composition Competition for his work *Sonata for Harpsichord*, published by The FJH Music Company Inc. and recorded by Elaine Funaro (*Into the Millennium*, Gasparo GSCD-331).

Since 1979, Edwin McLean has arranged the music of some of today's best known recording artists. Currently, he is senior editor as well as MIDI orchestrator for FJH Music.

Kevin Olson

Kevin Olson is an active pianist, composer, and faculty member at Elmhurst College near Chicago, Illinois, where he teaches classical and jazz piano, music theory, and electronic music. He holds a Doctor of Education degree from National-Louis University, and bachelor's and master's degrees in music composition and theory from Brigham Young University. Before teaching at Elmhurst College, he held a visiting professor position at Humboldt State University in California.

A native of Utah, Kevin began composing at the age of five. When he was 12, his composition *An American Trainride* received the Overall First Prize at the 1983 National PTA Convention in Albuquerque, New Mexico. Since then, he has been a composer-in-residence at the National Conference on Piano Pedagogy and has written music for the American Piano Quartet, Chicago a cappella, the Rich Matteson Jazz Festival, and several piano teachers associations around the country.

Kevin maintains a large piano studio, teaching students of a variety of ages and abilities. Many of the needs of his own piano students have inspired over 40 books and solos published by The FJH Music Company Inc., which he joined as a writer in 1994.

Robert Schultz

Robert Schultz, composer, arranger, and editor, has achieved international fame during his career in the music publishing industry. The Schultz Piano Library, established in 1980, has included more than 500 publications of classical works, popular arrangements, and Schultz's original compositions in editions for pianists of every level from the beginner through the concert artist. In addition to his extensive library of published piano works, Schultz's output includes original orchestral works, chamber music, works for solo instruments, and vocal music.

Schultz has presented his published editions at workshops, clinics, and convention showcases throughout the United States and Canada. He is a long-standing member of ASCAP and has served as president of the Miami Music Teachers Association. Mr. Schultz's original piano compositions and transcriptions are featured on the compact disc recordings *Visions of Dunbar* and *Tina Faigen Plays Piano Transcriptions*, released on the ACA Digital label and available worldwide. His published original works for concert artists are noted in Maurice Hinson's *Guide to the Pianist's Repertoire, Third Edition*. He currently devotes his full time to composing and arranging, writing from his studio in Miami, Florida. In-depth information about Robert Schultz and The Schultz Piano Library is available at the Web site www.schultzmusic.com.

A great way to prepare for your duet performances is to use the CD in the following ways:

1) The first eight tracks are the duet performances of each piece. Enjoy listening to these duets anywhere, anytime! Listen to them casually (as background music) or attentively. After you have listened to the CD, you might discuss interpretation with your teacher and follow along with your score as you listen.

About the *primo* and *secondo* parts: (These Italian music terms are pronounced "PREE-moh" and "seh-KOHN-doh")

Remember that the *primo* part is always on the right-hand side of the book, while the *secondo* part is always on the left-hand side of the book. The *primo* part usually stays above middle C, while the *secondo* part usually stays below middle C.

2) The rest of the tracks are to help you prepare for your duet collaborations. The CD can be used as a practice partner because you can play along with the tracks! This is how it works:

Each duet part has a practice track. Practice with this track so that you can learn to play steadily, accurately, and without stopping. You will hear the pianist counting one measure out loud, in order to indicate exactly when the piece begins and what the tempo is.

Once you feel completely confident about playing along with your own piano part, then try playing with the recording of your partner's part.